Chi's Sweet Home

チーズ スイート ホーム

8

Konami Kanata

contents
homemade 129~146+

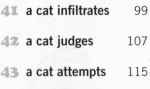

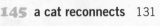
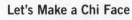

SKOOT—

WAFF WAFF WAFF WAFF

MEOW

3

4

5

STRETCH

SWIP

SWIP

JUST A LITTLE MORE!

MEOW!

HUH?

AH ...

WHOOPS

TUCK

SHOMP

WOW

MEOW

AWE-
SOME!

MEOW

CHI,
AREN'T
YOU
AMAZING
!

I DON'T
KNOW, BUT
THAT WAS
AMAZING!

the end

CHI WANTS TO PLAY, TOO!

VROOM

MEOW

CHI, YOU'LL BE RUN OVER.

VRRM

SNATCH

MIYA

MOMMY, WE GONNA PLAY?

CRUNCHIES? I HAVE SOME LEFT.

DADDY, CAN WE PLAY?!

MIYA

DASH—

AREN'T YOU SO SPOILED, CHI.

TMP TMP....

I WONDER IF HE'S OUT THERE?

MEOW

CHI'LL BE BACK!

HOP

IS HE, IS HE?

MYA

MYA

...

DITHER

HITHER THITHER

HAH

HAH

HA

IS HE?

IS HE?

AHH...

HE IS!

HEY HEY!

MEOW MEOW

HEYYY!

MEOW

DASH...!

COCCHI!

MEOW

MIYA

I KNEW YOU'D BE HERE!

HA

HA

MEOW

CHI KNEW SHE'D FIND YOU HERE.

DID COCCHI THINK SO, TOO?

MYA

MRR TSK

MRR

I JUST HAPPENED TO PASS BY.

MRR

SO IS YOUR STOMACH BETTER?

HUH?

MYA

MYA

MIYA

HOW'D YOU KNOW?

MRR

I AIN'T TELLING...

MIYA

WHA?

MRR SO...

MERR

WHAT DO YA WANT FROM ME?

MEOW

LET'S PLAY!

16

the end

MEOW

HEY, CHI FOUND THIS FIRST.

GRIP TUG

MRR

IF I TAKE IT, IT'S MINE...

AWE-
SOME...

LIKE...

MEOW

DO YOU
GET IT,
COCCHI?

HRN
?

MRR

AWESOME,
THAT'S
LIKE...

MRR

WHAT
COULD
IT BE?

MYA

MRR

SUSPI-
CIOUS
...

LET'S
JUST
CHECK
IT OUT.

MRR

I CAN'T SEE ALL THE WAY IN...

MRR

MEOW

NOPE.

MRR

NIUTUT

I'M GONNA CHECK.

MEOW

NIUTUT

CHI'S GOING FIRST.

SHUV

PLUSH

MEOW

SOME-
THING'S IN
THERE!

ALL
RIGHT!

MERR

MYA

IT WAS
PLUSHY.

WHAT
IS IT?

MYA
MYA

MRR
MRR

IT'S
AWE-
SOME!

RUMMAGE
RUMMAGE
RUMMAGE

PLUSH

MRR

THERE
IT IS—

HUH
?

MRR

OUCH!

SCRATCH

...

...

...

...

MEOW

HUH, IT WAS JUST COCCHI'S PAW.

TSK, IT WAS JUST YOU.

MRR

MRR

WE STRUCK OUT.

GREEN PARK

MIYA

WHAT DO WE DO NEXT?

MRR

HUH ?!

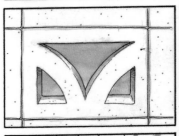

the end

I'LL GO IN FIRST!

MRR

MEOW

CHI'S FIRST.

MEOW

CHI IS!

I AM!

MRR

OUCH!

MRR

MVA

NOS!

MYA

HUH? WHY "OF COURSE"?

WHY, WHY?

MIYA

MRR

W-WELL ...

MRR?!

THAT'S BE-CAUSE...

GADE

MERR

A SCARY THING MIGHT APPEAR.

MYA

CHI'S ISN'T SCARED OF ANY-THING.

OH ...

29

MIYA

MRR ALREADY SCARED, HUH?

MIYA THERE AREN'T ANY SCARY THINGS?

I WONDER ...

MRR SMIRK

MRR LET'S GO.

MRR SO SUSPICIOUS ...

SLINK SLINK NO SCARY THINGS, PLEASE!

SLINK

SLINK

SNAP

EEEK

MEOW R

WOAH

MERRG

BOING

BOING

WH— WHAT IS IT?

MRR

MYA...

SOMETHING SNAPPY—

MYA

HERE.

MRR

HUH?

MEOW

PHEW, WHAT A RELIEF.

MRR

HOW COULD YOU BE AFRAID OF THAT?

MRR

WHAT'S BACK THERE?

SNEAK

SNEAK

NOTHING SCARY, PLEASE.

MEOW

SLINK SLINK

SLINK

BOING

MEOWR

EEEK

WHOA

MERRR

BOING

MRR

WHAT NOW?

MERR

HOW COULD GRASS FRIGHTEN YOU?

the end

MEOW

WOW

MRR

TSK. IT'S JUST A BIT OF SKY.

MEOW

SO SMALL BUT...

MYA

WHAT IS IT?

IS IT ALIVE?

MRR

MEOW

MRR

BOING

BOING

IT'S NOT ATTACK-ING BACK.

MIYA

THEN CHI'S GONNA BOP IT, TOO!

MEOW

BOP BOP

MRR

SNIF SNIF

BOP

IT'S NOT ALIVE AND IT'S NOT FOOD, EITHER.

MRR

WHAT COULD IT BE?

IT MUST BE FOR BOPPING!

MEOW

SEE?

MEOW

BOP BOP BOP BOP

MRR

I GUESS SO.

THERE'S SOME-THING HERE!

MEOW

39

MRR WHAT THE HECK?

SUSPICIOUS... MRR MEOW DEFINITELY.

MEOW WHAT COULD IT BE? REACH

GRIP

TUG

MYA HUH? SLOTH

SLAK!

the end

homemade 134: a cat is pursued

WATCH CHI JUMP!

HEH HEH !

UGH

43

MEOW

CHI'S REALLY FAST!

SKOOT—...

MERR

I'M WAY FASTER!

SKOOT—

MEOW

CHI'S EVEN FASTER!

DASH

MEOW

SEE?

SKOOT

RUFF

!

MEOW

EEK EEK EEK !

MRR

HEH, IT'S JUST A DOG.

HMPH

WHA?

44

YOU SEE... A DOG'S GOT A LEASH,

SO IT CAN'T MOVE FREELY.

MRR

MRR

TUT, TUT.

PANT PANT

TUG

MEOW

AH-HAH.

SEE?

MRR

MEOW

COCCHI SURE KNOWS A LOT.

BOING

OH!

45

RUFF

DASH

! FRSK !

MEOWR

YIKES!

MRRR

RUN, CHI!

PANT

PANT

MEOR

EEK! OH NOS!

DASH——

SNAP

MYA

OH, RIGHT!

MYA

LET'S HIDE!

MRR

HIDE?

MEOW

BLACKIE SHOWED ME HOW.

47

48

49

the end

YIPE!

RUFF RUFF

FSSK

STAY AWAY!

FSSK

DON'T COME NEAR ME!

MERR

CHI, HURRY UP AND CLIMB!

SKFF

SKFF SKFF SKFF

LICK

!

MEGOWR

SKAT

MRR...

CH-CHI, YOU ARE FAST!

HA HA HA

STOP THAT.

Y Y A A P P

RUFF RUFF RUFF

MEOW WE'RE SAFE.

MRR

HUH?

HEY, YOU...

MRR

MI

HMM?

MRR! SMELL LIKE DOG! ?! WHA?

SNF SNF SNF

CHI SMELLS LIKE DOG! MEOW

MRR IT'S CUZ THAT DOG LICKED YOU JUST NOW.

MEOW BUT COCCHI SMELLS LIKE DOG TOO!

!

MRR YOU GOT IT ON ME.

MEOW YOU SMELL WEIRD!

LICK LICK LICK LICK LICK LICK

I CAN'T REACH... MIYA

LICK LICK MRR WHAT CAN YOU DO...

MYA THANK YOU. MRR YOU MEAN "SOR-RY."

54

ALL RIGHT!

MRR

MRR

WE'VE GOT OUR SMELLS BACK!

MEOW

YEAH, WE DID!

NEAT! *MEOW*

MYA RIGHT YUP *MRR*

HOW DO WE GET DOWN?

MEOW

WE'RE UP REALLY HIGH.

REALLY HIGH.

MRR

MRR

IT'S NO USE.

MEOW

LET'S JUMP OVER THERE.

MRR

WHERE?

SAY—

MIYA

MIYA

ON TOP OF THAT WALL.

MRR!

WHAT?!

MRR

NO WAY.

IT'S TOO NAR- ROW.

MRR

AND IT'S FAR DOWN.

MRR

MEOW

I'M SURE WE'LL BE FINE.

GEH

HUH?!

MRR

WHY'S THAT?

MEOW

JUST A HUNCH.

HUH?!

58

the end

MRR

HEH HEH!

MRR A LITTLE MISSTEP BUT I GOT DOWN.

MRR NOW IT'S YOUR TURN.

...

HEY?

MRR

WHAT, ARE YOU SCARED?

MRR

MRR GO AHEAD. WITH BOUNCE IN YOUR BODY YOU'LL LAND JUST FINE.

"BOUNCE" IN MY BODY?

BOUNCE?

WHAT'S "BOUNCE"?

MIYA

CHI'S GOT NO BOUNCE.

MRR

DON'T BE FOOLISH, YOU DO.

MRR

YOU'RE A CAT, AFTER ALL.

CHI'S NOT A CAT.

MEOW

WHAT?

MEOW!

CHI'S LIKE MOMMY, DADDY AND YOHEY.

MEOW

CHI'S NOT A CAT!

MRR

WHAT SORT OF EXCUSE IS THAT?

MRR

YOU'RE A CAT!

 HAVE FAITH, YOU'RE A CAT!

MRR

 MRR? YOU PLAN TO STAY THERE FOREVER?

MYA NOS.

I'M GOING HOME.

MYA

 MRR

THEN YOU GOTTA JUMP!

 MYA

I CAN'T DO IT!

MYA CHI'S NOT A CAT!

 MRR! JUMP, CHI!

MRR! JUMP!

 SPRING

SHU-UUMP

OH!

THAT'S MY BOUNCE!

MERR!

YOU DID IT, CHI!

HOP

SPROING

SPROING

the end

LATER.

MRR

TIP TIP TIP····

YOU'RE A CAT.

YOU'VE GOT BOUNCE, CUZ YOU'RE A CAT!

THAT WAS SOME BOUNCE, CHI!

YOU'RE A CAT!

HMPH!

MEOW
MEOW
WEIRD!
MEOW
SO WEIRD!
MEOW
I'M NOT!

TIP TIP TIP TIP

MEOW
I'M HUNGRY.
MEOW
BETTER HURRY HOME!
DASH

MEOW
I'M HOME!

MEOW
I'M HUNGRY.
MIYA
MOMMY!

FOUND SOME!

MYA

GRIP

MYA

WHOA

MIYA

THERE MUST BE SOMETHING HERE, RIGHT?

SALTED POTATO CHIPS

HMM?

HM?

LAP LAP

HEY
?

HMM
?

MYA?

WHAT'S THIS?

SRF SRF

LICK

MEOW

I DON'T WHAT IT IS BUT...

KSH

MEOW

I'M DIGGING IN!

BYE, YOHEI.

BYE, YOHEI'S MOM.

OKAY

BYE-BYE.

TMP TMP TMP

OH, IT'S CHI.

OH?

HEY, CHI,

THAT'S NOT...

I'M HOME!

WHAT'S WRONG?

CHI! THAT'S —

the end

77

SHINE SHINE

MIYA

IT'S SO BRIGHT!

AHH!

MYA

IT'S WARM HERE!

PLOP

MEOW

THIS IS IT!

CHI!

WHAT ARE YOU UP TO?

ARGH

MEOW

YOU'RE IN MY WAY, YOHEY.

I'M IN YOUR SHADE...

MYA

MYA YOUR SHADE!

HUH? WHAT?

AHH

BRIGHT!

FLOP

IT'S NICE AND WARM HERE.

YOHEY AND CHI, THE SAME.

79

IT SURE IS WARM HERE.

MIU

PURR PURR PURR

WHERE WAS THAT?

SQUEEZE

— BUT —

the end

!

MEOW

WHAT IS THAT THING?

WHAT IS IT?

MIYA

WHAT'S IT DOING ?

PING

PING

PING

SUFF

SUFF

SUFF

SUFF

SLINK

OH

MYA

HOP

SLILINK

HEY

MYA

HOP

SHFT

SUSPICIOUS!

TURN

NOWHERE TO RUN. SHAK SHAK

MEOWR

I'VE GOT YA!

WHUM

ZA SH

RIBBIT

SMSH

MYA?

the end

HA
HA

CHI LOOKS LIKE SHE'S HAVING FUN IN THERE.

M
Y
A

HRN?

CHI LOVES TO PLAY WITH YOHEI.

SHE SURE DOES.

PAT

EVEN IF SHE'S PLAYING HER OWN GAMES.

RUB RUB RUB

PURR PURR PURR

WANT SOME MILK, CHI?

MILK 3.5

!

RISE

MEOW MOMMY'S GOT MILK!
HOP
DASH—...

MEOW THANK YOU.

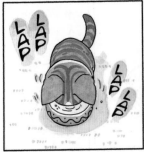
LAP LAP LAP LAP

HA HA HA...

AND OUR NEXT STORY IS...

VROOE VROOE

MRR

MRR

HUH?

THAT VOICE ...

TURN

MRR

CHI—

MRR

COME OUT, CHI!

IT'S COCCHI!

BUT THE MIULK...

MRR

COME OUT, CHI.

MRR

CHI!

HM, WHERE'S CHI?

MEOW

BE RIGHT BACK.

MEOW

I'LL HAVE THE MIULK LATER.

BOUND

SKOOT

96

the end

OH—

WOW!

YAY!  MEOW

 HAVEN'T I FOUND A COOL PLACE! TURN

 MERR WHAT DO YA THINK? HEH HEH!

 MIYA WHERE IS CHI?

 MRR HUH?!

SNEAK

SNEAK

FOUND YA!

MRR

MYA

EEK!

BAM

POP

MEOW

YOU FOUND ME.

MRR

OH!

MYA

AHH

SWID SWID

MEOW

WOW

SNAKE

SNAKE

MOZO

CHI'S GONNA DO THAT TOO!

MEOW

YEAH, PULL IT!

PULL, PULL!

MRR

MEOW

WE CAN'T PULL IT ALL, HUH?

MEOW

HAH

HAH

OH

MRR

MYA

WHAT?

GRIN

SMAK

SMAK

102

MRR

HEH HEH... NOW THIS IS IT!

MRR

I'M MAKING THIS MY NEW SLEEPING PLACE.

CHI'S GOING OVER THERE TOO!

MEOW

THWAK

MEOW

MINOR FAIL...

SLIDE

HUH?

THUNK

MEOW

TAKE THAT!

MEOW

MEOW

HEAVE HO!

SHOOM

the end

SLIDE

SHOO SHOO

YOU PRANK-STER CATS!

PHEW

OH, BOY.

TURN...

SKOOT

WHOA!

WHAT DO I DO?

HUFF

HUFF

CLEANERS

MRR

HAH— THAT WAS SURE SCARY, HUH, CHI?

HUFF

MRR...

CHI?

HUH?

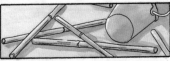

I'LL HIDE IN HERE FOR A BIT.

MEOW

COMING THIS WAY...

PEEK

GRIN

ONCE I'M ALONE, I'LL SCRAM.

OH!

114

the end

THERE MUST BE ANOTHER WAY OUT.

MEOW

HOW ABOUT BACK HERE?

MYA

CAN'T GET OUT THROUGH HERE.

MYA

HOW ABOUT THAT GAP OVER THERE?

MYA

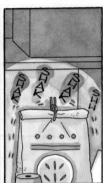

SHK

MYA

THAT WASN'T IT.

THAT NOOK LOOKS SUSPICIOUS.

MYA

MEOW

IT'S A LITTLE TIGHT.

THIS BETTER OPEN UP.

MEOW

MEOW

IT WON'T?

AND THIS SIDE IS NARROW TOO.

MEOW

MEOW

HAH!

MYA

THAT WASN'T IT, EITHER.

MYA

MAYBE UP THERE?

SRIP

OPEN, OPEN!

MYA

MYA

IT WON'T?

SKRE SKRE

WHERE WILL IT?

MIYA

OH...

MEOW

THIS WAS GONNA BE COCCHI'S "SLEEPING PLACE."

HEH HEH

118

MYA I'M GONNA STEP IN.

MYA I'M GONNA REST A BIT.

FLOP

...

AT THIS RATE, THIS WILL BE CHI'S SLEEPING PLACE.

GRRRR

I'M HUNGRY.

GRRRR

MIULK

I SHOULD HAVE DRANK IT ALL.

GRRR!

BLOCKS

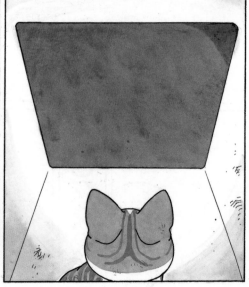

the end

MRR CHI

HEY, CHI! MERR

MRR WHERE ARE YA?

CHI MRR

MAYBE SHE WENT TO THE PARK? MRR

TIP TIP

NYO

CHI?

SPLASH

NYU WELL, I HAVEN'T SEEN HER YET.

THAT CHI... **HRM** DID SHE DITCH OUR PLAYING AND GO HOME?

M R R TSK

HOP

M R R

LIKE I CARE ABOUT THAT ONE.

TIP TIP TIP TIP

SCREECH SCREEEK

SHOOM M R G ZING

WHAT'YA DOING, THAT WAS DAN-GEROUS!

MRR!!

DID SOMETHING HAPPEN TO HER?

SAY, YOHEI...

IS CHI OVER THERE?

SHE'S NOT WITH ME.

HOW ODD.

WHAT'S UP?

LOOKS LIKE CHI HASN'T COME BACK.

SHE'S BEEN OUT FOR A WHILE.

IT'LL BE NIGHT SOON.

SHE MUST BE HAVING A GOOD TIME THEN, HUH?

HA HA HA

BUT SHE BARELY TOUCHED HER BELOVED MILK...

I LEFT IT OUT FOR HER.

UH LIKE WHAT?

LIKE SHE CAN'T COME HOME?

YUP

IS SHE LOST?

DID SOME- THING HAPPEN TO HER?

HITHER THITHER

FLOP

THAT MIGHT BE IT.

MAYBE SHE FOL- LOWED SOME- ONE,

OR WAS PICKED UP?

MEOW

CHI'S TRUST- ING.

AND SO CUTE.

PROUD

127

ALSO ...

DAN-GERS?

THERE ARE SO MANY DANGERS OUTDOORS FOR CATS.

SHE COULD CLIMB UP HIGH AND GET STUCK.

THERE ARE RIVERS AND DITCHES.

SHE COULD BE HURT AND UNABLE TO MOVE.

AND ...

AND?

VROOOM
BEEP
SKREE

SKREE
CHEEERRU!

LET'S GO LOOK FOR CHI!

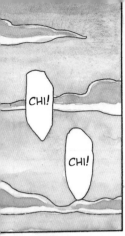

the end

CHI

WE HAVE NO CLUE...

WHEN CHI GOES OUT...

WHERE DOES SHE GO?

WHAT DOES SHE DO?

YOU SAID IT.

CHI

WHERE ARE YOU?

PANT PANT PANT

SO WHERE'D YOU GO OFF TO?

MRR

MRR

I WAS WOR-RIED!

I DIDN'T GO OFF ANYWHERE.

MEOW

MRR

AND HOW DID YA GET SO DIRTY?

mer mer mer

HUH?

MIYA

MYA

REALLY?

MRR

DID YA STUMBLE INTO SOME HOLE?!

MEOW NO WAY! MRR WOAH BAM HOP

UGH MEOW RUN AWAY! DASH—

MRR MY TURN! BLAM HOP MYA WHOA

MRR WHAM MEOW DON'T BLAM INTO ME. HOP

MEOW YAY, RUN! MEOW I'M GOING HOME! DASH—

MRR MIYA YOUR HOME ISN'T THAT WAY. WHAT?

CAW CAW CAW

CHI

WHERE ARE YOU? CHI HOW MUCH TERRITORY CAN A KITTEN COVER ON HER OWN? CHI

CHI WHERE ARE YOU NOW?

133

GOING HOME

MYA

TO MY MIULK!

AHHH

CHI

CHI!

HEY, CHI!

WOW!

MEOW
MEOW

DASH

MEOW

EVERYONE, I'M BACK!

LET'S HAVE SOME MIULK!

THANK GOODNESS.

I'M GLAD FOR YOU.

CHI'S DIRTY.

136

MEOW

MIULK ♡

MEOW

MIULK ♡

TMP TMP TMP

MEOW

CHI STILL HAD MIULK LEFT, RIGHT?

OK, READY?

YUP

HUH?

HEY?

RZLLK

the end

FWIING

HUH?

CHI LOOKS WEIRD!

IT'S CALLED AN ELIZABETHAN COLLAR.

IT'S USED TO PREVENT HER FROM RUBBING HER EYE.

...

AH

GOOD IDEA.

FOOM
FOOM
FOOM
FOOM

TURN

TURN

MEOW

DADDY, I CAN'T TAKE THIS THING OFF!

TAKE IT OFF FOR ME!

MEOW

GOOD GIRL.

PAT PAT

WHAT?!

OH, THE ITCHIES...

ZING ZING

HEY?

SKFF SKFF

MEOW

HEY?

AH, IT DOES GUARD HER EYES.

I CAN'T REACH!

MEOW

GOOD IDEA.

SKFF SKFF

HAH~

CHI'S HUNGRY

AND THIRSTY.

TIP TIP TIP

EVEN WHEN SHE GETS BETTER, SHE'LL STAY HOME AT FIRST.

YEAH.

FOOD, FOOD.

TIP TIP TIP

MYA

HUH?

HMM?

MEOW

A RUDE SURPRISE ...

TIP TIP TIP

144

KLUNK

MYA

HEY?

CHI'S BUMPING INTO THINGS EVERYWHERE SHE WALKS.

?

WHAT'S GOING ON?

SHE'S YET TO FATHOM HER NEW WIDTH.

WELL, IT DID CHANGE SUDDENLY.

MEOW

HEY?

ZZASH

MEOW

HMMM?

SKRFF

HUH?

YOU HOPE TO GET THROUGH THAT?

TIP TIP TIP

145

the end

Extra
Chi's Sweet Origami!

Let's Make a Chi Face!!

Copy or cut out the image to the right and fold using the following instructions.

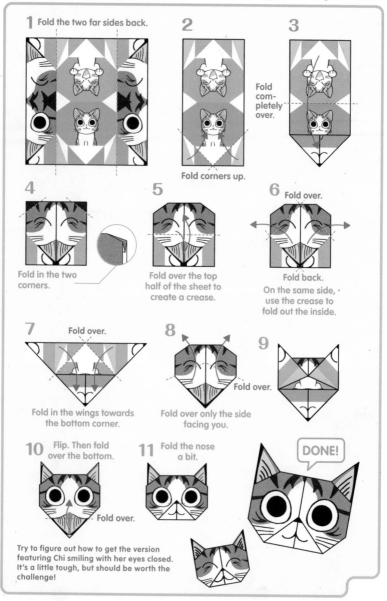

1 Fold the two far sides back.

2 Fold corners up.

3 Fold completely over.

4 Fold in the two corners.

5 Fold over the top half of the sheet to create a crease.

6 Fold over. Fold back. On the same side, use the crease to fold out the inside.

7 Fold over. Fold in the wings towards the bottom corner.

8 Fold over only the side facing you. Fold over.

9

10 Flip. Then fold over the bottom. Fold over.

11 Fold the nose a bit.

DONE!

Try to figure out how to get the version featuring Chi smiling with her eyes closed. It's a little tough, but should be worth the challenge!

Origami (instructions on facing page)

Let's try to fold our way to both
of Chi's origami faces!

Chi's Sweet Home, volume 8

Translation - Ed Chavez
Production - Hiroko Mizuno
            Tomoe Tsutsumi

Translation provided by Vertical, Inc., 2012
Published by Vertical, Inc., New York

Originally published in Japanese as *Chiizu Suiito Houmu* by Kodansha, Ltd., 2009-2010
Chiizu Suiito Houmu first serialized in *Morning*, Kodansha, Ltd., 2004-

This is a work of fiction.

ISBN: 978-1-935654-35-3

Manufactured in China

First Edition

Second Printing

Vertical, Inc.
451 Park Avenue South, 7th Floor
New York, NY 10016
www.vertical-inc.com

Special thanks to: K. Kitamoto